SUPPANDI, WHY HAVE YOU PUT THE EYEDROPS ON FATHER'S EYELIDS INSTED OF INTO HIS EYES?

IT'S WRITTEN HERE: FOR EXTERNAL USE ONLY.

SUPPANDI'S FORMER BOSSES ON SUPPANDI ...

"HE'S DUMB, DUMBER, DUMBEST!"

"HE USED TO DRIVE ME CRAZY! I USED TO PULL OUT BUNCHES OF MY HAIR IN FRUSTRATION!"

"HE'S A MONSTER! HE WANTED TO REMOVE MY WRINKLES WITH A HOT IRON!"

"A STRANGE CASE, DOCTOR! HE SEEMS TO BE MAD AT SOMEONE!"

SuppanDi... SuppanDi!... I'll strangle him!... Grrr...

Suppandi says:
"I BRING HAPPINESS AND JOY WHEREVER I GO. NOBODY WHOM I'VE WORKED FOR CAN EVER FORGET ME!"

SUPPANDI HAS A REMEDY
This was the very first Suppandi story to appear in Tinkle.

SUPPANDI WAS A FOOLISH YOUNG BOY WHO LIVED IN A LITTLE VILLAGE WITH HIS GRANDMOTHER. ONE DAY—

ACHI, YOU'RE HOT ALL OVER.

I THINK I HAVE FEVER, MY CHILD. GO FETCH A DOCTOR.

I'LL GO AT ONCE.

ON HIS WAY, HE HAD TO PASS A FORGE.

HSSS

WHY DID YOU PUT THAT RED HOT IRON INTO THE WATER, SIR?

TO COOL IT.

SEE HOW COLD IT HAS BECOME.

IF WATER CAN COOL A RED HOT IRON SO FAST, WHY NOT...

SUPPANDI RAN BACK HOME...

...DREW A BUCKET OF WATER FROM THE WELL...

...AND WENT IN.

HAVE YOU BROUGHT THE DOCTOR?

NO. WE DON'T NEED HIM.

THIS WILL CURE YOU.

YIEEEE!

WHAT ARE YOU DOING?

LIE STILL, GRAND-MOTHER.

AHH!

HELP! HELP ME, SOMEBODY!

THE NEIGHBOURS HEARING HER SCREAM RUSHED IN...

...AND CAUGHT HOLD OF THE BOY.

WHAT ARE YOU DOING, YOU IDIOT?

OOOOH!

GRANDMOTHER, ARE YOU ALL RIGHT?

GET A DOCTOR SOMEBODY.

SHE DOESN'T NEED A DOCTOR.

LET ME...

GIVE ME THAT BUCKET!

THE VILLAGERS BROUGHT A DOCTOR...

...AND THE OLD WOMAN RECOVERED IN A FEW DAYS.

IF YOU HAD LET ME THROW THAT COLD WATER ON YOU, GRANDMOTHER...

...YOUR FEVER WOULD HAVE GONE ON THE VERY FIRST DAY.

SUPPANDI GOES TO THE BAZAAR

ONCE SUPPANDI WAS ASKED TO BUY SOME COCONUT OIL AND SOME GHEE FROM THE BAZAAR.

HERE IS THE MONEY. NOW, GO. YOU SHOULD BE BACK WHEN I'VE FINISHED BATHING.

I'LL TAKE THIS BOTTLE. I CAN USE IT FOR BOTH THE OIL AND THE GHEE.

THAT WAY, I'LL HAVE TO CARRY ONLY ONE BOTTLE AND···

···WITH LESS WEIGHT IN MY HANDS, I SHOULD BE ABLE TO GET BACK FASTER!

AT THE MARKET—

HERE'S THE OIL. NOW, WHERE SHALL I POUR THE GHEE?

PROUDLY, SUPPANDI TURNED THE BOTTLE OVER.

HERE, POUR THE GHEE INTO THIS HOLLOW.

INTO THIS HOLLOW? BUT··· HOW···?

DON'T ASK FOOLISH QUESTIONS, MISTER. JUST DO AS YOU'RE TOLD.

AS YOU WISH.

SUPPANDI TOOK THE BOTTLE AND STARTED WALKING HOME — VERY, VERY CAREFULLY.

THERE YOU ARE. WHERE IS THE GHEE?

HERE.

AND THE OIL?

HERE.

SPLASH

IDIOT! MORON!

GET OUT OF MY SIGHT.

AH, WELL! CLEVER PEOPLE LIKE ME WILL ALWAYS BE ILL-TREATED BY THE WORLD! ONE HAS TO LIVE WITH IT!!

THE EXPANDING CHAPPALS

SUPPANDI! I'D LIKE TO HAVE A PAIR OF THOSE NEW PLASTIC CHAPPALS.

YES, DADIMA.

WHY DON'T YOU GO AND BUY ME A PAIR— HERE'S THE MONEY.

OKAY.

ON THE WAY HOME FROM THE SHOE SHOP—

WHY ARE YOU LEAVING SO MUCH SPACE BETWEEN THE TWO RAILS?

BECAUSE WHEN IT'S HOT, THE RAILS WILL EXPAND AND BECOME LONGER.

OH, SO HEAT EXPANDS THINGS AND MAKES THEM LARGER?

YES, OF COURSE. THAT'S ELEMENTARY!

BACK HOME—

DADIMA, HERE ARE YOUR NEW PLASTIC CHAPPALS.

THANKS, SUPPANDI. LET ME PUT THEM ON.

OH, DEAR! THEY'RE A SIZE TOO SMALL —GO BACK TO THE SHOP AND BRING ANOTHER PAIR.

I HAVE BETTER IDEA!

I'LL ROAST THEM ON THIS 'TAVA'...THEY WILL BECOME BIGGER...

THEY MUST BE THE RIGHT SIZE BY NOW.

WHAT?! WHAT'S HAPPENING? TO THE CHAPPALS?

DADIMA, DADIMA! YOUR CHAPPALS ARE DISAPPEARING!

DISAPPEARING?

WHEN I FIND THE FOOL WHO KEPT THEM ON THE TAWA, I'LL MAKE HIM DISAPPEAR!

SUPPANDI GETS VISITORS

NO ONE, YOU UNDERSTAND?

YES SIR.

SUPPANDI, OPEN UP!

I WON'T!

DIDN'T YOU TELL ME NOT TO LET ANYONE IN?

OH, THIS IS TOO MUCH!

I'M THE MASTER OF THE HOUSE, YOU ASS! NOW OPEN THE DOOR!

I WON'T

I KNOW YOU'RE ONLY TESTING ME.

OPEN UP, I SAY!

OPEN THE DOOR!

HAVE I PASSED THE TEST?

YOU HAVE! YOU HAVE!

NOW OPEN THE DOOR!

NOW THAT I'VE PASSED THE TEST, I HOPE YOU'LL RAISE MY SALARY, SIR.

TAMING THE FLAME

FIRE, FIRE!

THE KITCHEN IS ON FIRE, SIR.

OH!

SUPPANDI! COME ON, WE'LL OVERTURN THE VESSEL OF WATER AND PUT OUT THE FIRE. SIMPLE...

NO, SIR, WE MUSTN'T. IT'LL MAKE IT RAGE MORE FIERCELY...

...YOU SEE, THE WATER IN THAT VESSEL IS BOILING HOT!

?

TINKLE TRICKS & TREATS ① TRICKS & TREATS

A

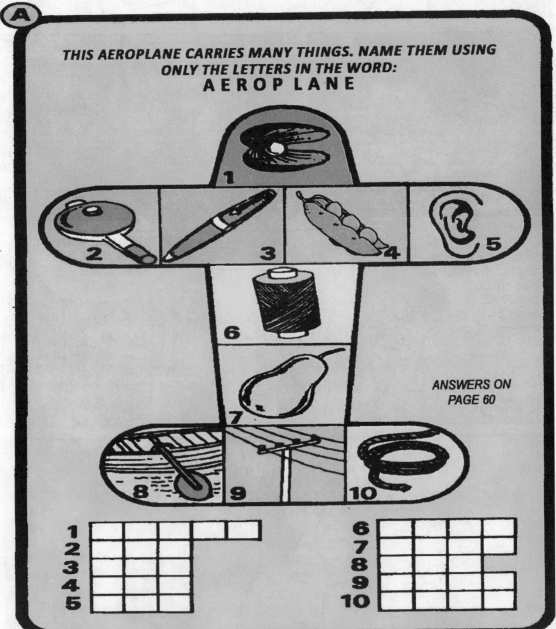

THIS AEROPLANE CARRIES MANY THINGS. NAME THEM USING ONLY THE LETTERS IN THE WORD:
A E R O P L A N E

ANSWERS ON PAGE 60

B

CAN YOU NAME THE COUNTRIES REPRESENTED BY THE FLAGS?

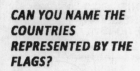

1 ⬚⬚⬚⬚⬚   ⬚⬚⬚⬚⬚   3 ⬚⬚⬚ ⬚⬚⬚⬚⬚

4 ⬚⬚⬚⬚⬚⬚   5 ⬚⬚⬚⬚⬚⬚⬚⬚⬚⬚   ⬚⬚⬚⬚⬚⬚   7 ⬚⬚⬚⬚⬚⬚⬚⬚

C

OUR FRIEND HAS LEARNT A LESSON TODAY – A LESSON AN OLD PROVERB TEACHES.

WHAT IS THE PROVERB?

⬚ ⬚⬚⬚ ⬚⬚ ⬚⬚⬚⬚ ⬚⬚ ⬚⬚⬚⬚⬚ ⬚⬚⬚ ⬚⬚ ⬚⬚⬚ ⬚⬚⬚⬚

Make your own toy
BOOMERANG

YOU WILL NEED: A PIECE OF STIFF CARD PAPER, TRACING PAPER, A PENCIL AND A PAIR OF SCISSORS.

THE BOOMERANG IS A WEAPON USED BY THE ABORIGINES OF AUSTRALIA. WHEN THROWN, IF IT MISSES THE TARGET, IT RETURNS TO THE MAN WHO HAS THROWN IT.

1. TRACE OUT THIS SHAPE.

2. PLACE THE TRACING ON THE CARD AND CUT ALONG THE LINE.

3. YOUR BOOMERANG IS READY. NOW STICK IT UNDER THE NAIL OF YOUR LEFT THUMB LIKE THIS.

4. NEXT FLICK IT WITH THE FIRST FINGER OF YOUR RIGHT HAND LIKE THIS.

YOUR BOOMERANG WILL FLY THROUGH THE AIR AND RETURN TO YOU, LIKE THIS!

TEA, COFFEE OR QUESTIONS?

SUPPANDI ONCE TOOK UP THE JOB OF A WAITER IN A RESTAURANT—

...AND REMEMBER, YOU MUST ALWAYS DO THINGS THAT MAKE THE CUSTOMER FEEL IMPORTANT.

ONE WAY TO DO THIS IS TO ASK RELEVANT QUESTIONS...

YES, SIR!

AND SO—

WAITER! GET ME A CUP OF TEA.

HOT OR COLD?

ARE YOU JOKING? DOES ANYONE DRINK COLD TEA?! GET ME A CUP OF STEAMING HOT TEA.

YES, SIR!

...ER...WOULD YOU LIKE TO HAVE IT IN A CUP OR A GLASS OR A...

OR A WHAT? WHAT ELSE CAN YOU SERVE TEA IN?

...A MUG?

NOW WILL YOU GET A CUP OF TEA OR...

YES, SIR, YES, SIR.

Sports with SUPPANDI

How much do the bails placed on cricket wickets, weigh? I did some research and found that each weighs as much as a medium size lady's finger. Many of you may not know how much a lady's finger weighs. Well, it weighs as much as a small tomato. If you're wondering why I'm going on and on about tomatoes and things, it's because I like to be precise and lucid. I'm sure anyone who reads this will never forget how much a bail weighs!

I was once invited to play in a football match as one of the teams was short of players. Halfway through the match the referee awarded a Free Kick to the opposite team. I was appalled! Here I was merrily kicking the ball at every opportunity unaware that there were only a few Free Kicks. I quietly slipped out of the field before they could ask me to pay.

Golf and tennis require a lot of investment, but basketball is a poor man's game. Observe the net they throw the ball into. Always torn at the bottom. Once, in a spirit of service I climbed up a basketball pole at dead of night and stitched up the bottom of the net.
How grateful they must have been! But they never knew whom to thank. I firmly believe that all good work must be done anonymously, so I never told anyone I was the midnight tailor.

INFLATION

SUPPANDI, TAKE THIS 50-RUPEE NOTE AND BRING 2 KILOS OF RICE FROM THE MARKET.

YES, SIR.

BE CAREFUL WITH THE MONEY.

YOU CAN RELY ON ME, SIR.

LATER— **HERE YOU ARE, SIR...(PUFF)... 2 KILOS OF RICE AND THE CHANGE...(PUFF)...**

I THOUGHT YOU MIGHT LIKE TO KNOW...RICE WILL COST MORE FROM TOMORROW ONWARDS.

YOU FOOL! YOU SHOULD HAVE BOUGHT MORE RICE WITH THE CHANGE! YOU'D HAVE SAVED ME SOME MONEY.

I MUST KEEP THAT IN MIND... HMMM...

SOME DAYS LATER— **SUPPANDI, HERE'S TEN RUPEES. GO AND BUY A COPY OF TODAY'S NEWSPAPER.**

AT ONCE, SIR.

HERE YOU ARE, SIR. THE PRICE OF NEWSPAPERS WILL BE GOING UP FROM TOMORROW...

...SO I BOUGHT TEN COPIES OF TODAY'S ...... PAPER!

GRR...RR!

GETTING A REFUND

SUPPANDI, I WISH TO PARTICIPATE IN AN ART COMPETITION. GO AND PAY MY FEE: SEVENTY-FIVE RUPEES AT THE COMMUNITY HALL.

YES, SIR.

HERE, TAKE THIS HUNDRED-RUPEE NOTE AND BRING BACK TWENTY-FIVE RUPEES.

LATER—

HERE YOU ARE, SIR. THE RECEIPT AND TWENTY-FIVE RUPEES.

A FEW DAYS LATER—

OH NO! THE COMPETITION HAS BEEN CANCELLED THEY ARE REFUNDING THE MONEY AND TODAY IS THE LAST DAY.

GO AND COLLECT MY MONEY.

I'LL GO IMMEDIATELY!

TWO HOURS LATER—

I HOPE HE HAS COLLECTED THE REFUND... THE COUNTER IS OPEN ONLY TILL THREE O'CLOCK AND IT'S PAST THREE NOW.

AH! HERE HE COMES.

DID YOU GET MY MONEY?

SIR, AS I WAS GOING TO THE HALL I SUDDENLY REALISED THAT IF I AM TO GET BACK YOUR HUNDRED-RUPEE NOTE, I'LL HAVE TO RETURN THE MONEY THEY GAVE ME.

SO, PLEASE LET ME HAVE THAT TWENTY FIVE RUPEES BACK.

DRYING A SHIRT

SUPPANDI, GET MY SHIRT. QUICKLY! I'M LATE!

THE SHIRT IS STILL NOT DRY. I'LL GO ON THE TERRACE AND HANG IT UP IN THE SUN.

UH, THE WEATHER IS CLOUDY, NO SUN.

SOME TIME LATER —

WHY AREN'T YOU DRYING MY SHIRT?!

I AM DOING JUST THAT. I'VE PUT YOUR SHIRT IN THIS HOT WATER.

HOT WATER?! HOW IS HOT WATER GOING TO DRY MY SHIRT, YOU FOOL!!

IF THE SUN CAN DRY YOUR SHIRT ONLY BECAUSE IT IS HOT, WHY CAN'T HOT WATER DRY IT TOO?

TRICKS & TREATS TINKLE ②

A

WE HAVE DONE THE FIRST SUM FOR YOU. DO THE OTHERS IN THE SAME WAY. THEN ADD THE ANSWERS AND YOU WILL GET SOMETHING WE ALL LOVE.

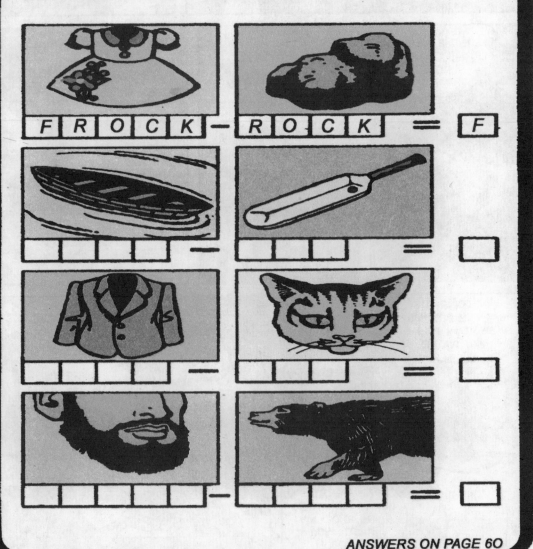

F R O C K − R O C K = F

ANSWERS ON PAGE 60

B

LOOK CAREFULLY AT THESE PICTURES. SOMETHING IMPORTANT IS MISSING IN EACH OF THEM. FIND OUT WHAT'S MISSING, FILL IT IN THE RIGHT SQUARE AND COMPLETE THE CROSSWORD.

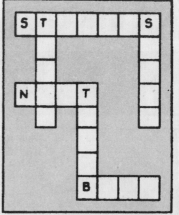

Make your own DANCING DOLLS

YOU WILL NEED:
A SQUARE SHEET OF THICK WHITE PAPER 6" X 6", A PENCIL, A PAIR OF SCISSORS, COLOUR PENCILS OR WATER COLOURS.

C

HERE IS AN ANIMAL DRAWN WITH THE HELP OF FIVE LETTERS. YOU WILL BE ABLE TO NAME THE ANIMAL, IF YOU FIND THE LETTERS AND WRITE THEM IN THE CORRECT ORDER.

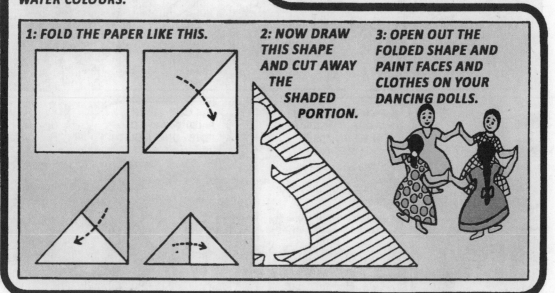

1: FOLD THE PAPER LIKE THIS.

2: NOW DRAW THIS SHAPE AND CUT AWAY THE SHADED PORTION.

3: OPEN OUT THE FOLDED SHAPE AND PAINT FACES AND CLOTHES ON YOUR DANCING DOLLS.

SUPPANDI SAVES A SHIRT

SUPPANDI!

HAVE YOU FINISHED IRONING MY SILK SHIRT?

YES, SIR!

THEN BRING IT. I HAVE TO GET DRESSED!

MASTER, I WAS IRONING AND SOMEONE KNOCKED ON THE DOOR. I WENT TO OPEN IT AND WHEN I CAME BACK I SMELT SOMETHING BURNING...

DON'T TELL ME YOU'VE BURNT MY SHIRT!

I...ER...YES.

OH, NO!

FORTUNATELY I HAVE ANOTHER SILK SHIRT IN THE CUPBOARD.

I KNOW THAT, SIR.

I CUT IT UP AND PATCHED UP THE ONE I BURNT!

BEGINNER'S COURSE

ONE DAY—

SUPPANDI, COME, I'LL TEACH YOU HOW TO DRIVE A CAR.

SIR, WHY HAVE YOU PUT THIS BOARD WITH AN 'L' WRITTEN ON IT?

SO THAT THE OTHERS WILL KNOW THAT YOU HAVE JUST STARTED LEARNING TO DRIVE.

L 2345

ONE DAY, AFTER SUPPANDI HAD LEARNT DRIVING—

SON! TODAY IS YOUR FIRST DAY AT SCHOOL. BE A GOOD BOY.

YES, PAPA.

SUDDENLY—

WAIT A MOMENT!

!?

?

LET ME PUT THIS 'L' ON YOUR BACK. THEN EVERYONE WILL KNOW THAT YOU HAVE JUST STARTED LEARNING.

UGH!

HOW CHEAP!

SUPPANDI, ALWAYS BUY THINGS FROM A PLACE WHERE YOU CAN GET THEM CHEAPEST.

YES, MASTER.

ONE DAY—

SUPPANDI, BUY SOME VEGETABLES.

YES, SIR.

LATER—

SUPPANDI, WHAT TOOK YOU SO LONG?

I WENT TO THE MAIN MARKET, SIR, TO GET CHEAP VEGETABLES.

BUT THAT IS SUCH A LONG WAY TO WALK. YOU MUST BE SO TIRED.

I AM NOT, SIR...

... I TOOK A TAXI TO AND FROM THE MARKET.

AARGH

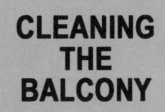

CLEANING THE BALCONY

SUPPANDI, WHY HAVEN'T YOU CLEANED THE BALCONY? LOOK AT THE NUMBER OF LEAVES STREWN HERE.

S... SORRY, SIR!

START CLEANING NOW. WHEN I COME BACK IN THE EVENING I SHOULD NOT SEE A SINGLE LEAF IN THE BALCONY.

O... OKAY.

THAT EVENING —

SUPPANDI, HAVE YOU FINISHED THE JOB I HAD ASKED YOU TO DO?

YES, SIR. THE BALCONY IS SPOTLESS. COME AND SEE.

WHEN THEY WENT THERE —

YAAGH! WHAT HAPPENED TO MY PLANTS? HOW DID THEY BECOME LEAFLESS?

YOU SAID THAT YOU DIDN'T WANT TO SEE A SINGLE LEAF IN THE BALCONY, SIR. SO I PLUCKED THEM ALL OUT!

OH NO!

Like everybody else I too have my favourite toons...
... the **DUMBBELLS!**

The **Dumbbells** Nattoo, Dattoo and Motu as their collective name suggests, are not the brightest of guys but they're an adventurous trio, and their escapades and blunders leave you in splits.

The brainchild of Prasad Iyer, former associate editor of Tinkle, the **DUMBBELLS** made its debut in Tinkle 133 published in July 1987, and ran for several months, delighting readers of all ages.

It was illustrated by Anand Mande whose sudden departure for greener pastures in 1990 brought a sudden end to the series, much to the disappointment of its numerous fans.

THE DUMBBELLS

in **Gold Bricks**

Script: Prasad Iyer
Illustrations: Anand Mande

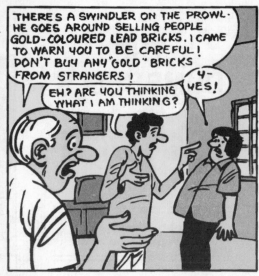

BUDDING TYCOON

SUPPANDI'S EMPLOYER WAS A SMALL-TIME BUSINESSMAN WHO TRIED TO TEACH HIM THE RUDIMENTS OF RUNNING A BUSINESS.

...SO REMEMBER, YOU MUST ALWAYS TRY TO MAKE A PROFIT. NOW TAKE THIS FIFTY RUPEE NOTE AND GIVE IT TO RATANLAL THE SHOP-KEEPER...

YES, SIR.

...HE WILL GIVE YOU A PACKAGE WHICH CONTAINS AN ELECTRIC MIXER. BRING IT BACK CAREFULLY.

AT RATANLAL'S —

MY EMPLOYER TOLD ME TO GIVE YOU THIS FIFTY RUPEE NOTE.

YES, I HAVE A PACKAGE FOR HIM.

THERE YOU ARE... SEE THAT YOU DON'T DROP IT ON THE WAY HOME.

HEY, IS THAT AN ELECTRIC MIXER YOU'RE CARRYING?

YES!

HOW MUCH DID YOU PAY FOR IT?

FIFTY RUPEES.

ONLY FIFTY RUPEES! WILL YOU SELL IT TO ME? I'LL GIVE YOU SEVENTY-FIVE.

DONE!

34

A PROFIT OF TWENTY-FIVE RUPEES. HEE, HEE! WHAT A SHREWD BUSINESSMAN I AM.

SOON I'LL BE A REAL TYCOON.

THERE YOU ARE! SUPPANDI WHERE IS THE MIXER?

I SOLD IT SIR, FOR SEVENTY-FIVE RUPEES. I MADE A NEAT PROFIT OF TWENTY-FIVE RUPEES.

WHAT?

I WAS CLEVER, WASN'T I?

YOU FOOL! THAT MIXER WAS WORTH TWO THOUSAND THREE HUNDRED RUPEES!

I WAS PURCHASING IT IN INSTALMENTS, I HAD TO PAY ONE LAST INSTALMENT.

THAT'S WHY I GAVE YOU FIFTY RUPEES - TO COMPLETE THE PAYMENT. NOW YOU'VE GONE AND SOLD IT FOR SEVENTY-FIVE RUPEES

I.... I....

YOU'RE FIRED! GET OUT!

WHAT A PITY. NOW I'LL NEVER GET TO BECOME A TYCOON.

THE HALFWAY MARK

RED SIGNAL

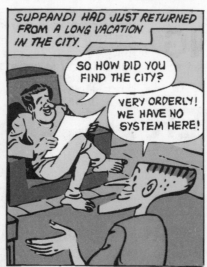

SUPPANDI HAD JUST RETURNED FROM A LONG VACATION IN THE CITY.

SO HOW DID YOU FIND THE CITY?

VERY ORDERLY! WE HAVE NO SYSTEM HERE!

WELL...NOW PLEASE GO TO THE MARKET AND BRING RICE AND SUGAR.

YES, SIR!

ON THE WAY—

A BULL!

THACK

IN THE CITY EVERYTHING THAT RUNS STOPS AT THE RED SIGNAL. BUT HERE, THIS BULL...AS I SAID THERE IS NO SYSTEM HERE

PLEASING THE CUSTOMER

SUPPANDI'S NEW MASTER WAS SETH DALPATRAM WHO RAN A PROVISION STORE. ONE DAY—

WHEN I GO HOME FOR LUNCH, YOU MUST ATTEND TO THE CUSTOMERS. I DON'T LIKE ANYONE LEAVING MY SHOP DISAPPOINTED. OKAY?

YES, SIR!

THAT'S THE SPIRIT.

THAT AFTERNOON—

OKAY, SUPPANDI, I AM GOING HOME!

YES, SIR!

REMEMBER WHAT I TOLD YOU IN THE MORNING— DON'T SEND ANYBODY AWAY DISAPPOINTED.

VERY WELL, SIR!

AN HOUR LATER—

DID ANYONE COME WHILE I WAS AWAY?

YES, SIR!

A MAN CAME WITH A VERY BIG GUN AND TOLD ME TO GIVE HIM ALL THE CASH. I MADE SURE HE DIDN'T LEAVE THE SHOP DISAPPOINTED!

PAYING GUEST

SUPPANDI'S MASTER HAD KEPT A PAYING GUEST WHO ALWAYS RETURNED VERY LATE. ONE NIGHT HE RETURNED LATER THAN USUAL—

WHERE HAVE YOU BEEN?

MY FRIENDS FORCED ME TO GO WITH THEM FOR A MOVIE!

OKAY, DON'T WORRY! I'LL LET YOU IN.

BUT WHAT ABOUT THE DOG? HE WILL START BARKING IF HE HEARS MY FOOTSTEPS.

I'VE GOT A SOLUTION FOR THAT TOO! NOW COME IN!

I AM LUCKY TO GET YOUR HELP!

I'VE ALMOST MADE IT. THANKS TO SUPPANDI!!

BANG
BANG
BANG
BANG

WHAT DID YOU DO THAT FOR, YOU FOOL!

I:...

I WANTED TO PREVENT THE DOG FROM HEARING YOUR FOOTSTEPS.

SUPPANDI OPENS SHOP

SUPPANDI HAD STARTED A BARBER'S SHOP. ONE MORNING—

I WANT A HAIR-CUT!

CERTAINLY!

YAWN!

OH, HE'S DOZED OFF! NEVER MIND, I'LL GO ON WITH MY WORK.

FIFTEEN MINUTES LATER WHEN THE CUSTOMER WOKE UP.

YEEEEEE!! WHAT HAVE YOU DONE, YOU FOOL?!

YOU MEAN YOU'RE NOT SATISFIED WITH MY WORK?

YOU CHEEKY RASCAL! YOU HAVE THE NERVE TO ASK ME THAT! OF COURSE I AM NOT SATISFIED!

KEEP CALM, SIR! KEEP CALM. THERE'S NO NEED TO GET ANGRY...

CAN'T YOU READ THAT SIGN OVER THERE?

CUSTOMERS' HAIR RETURNED CHEERFULLY IF NOT SATISFIED.

HARD OF HEARING

SUPPANDI'S EMPLOYER WAS AN EAR-NOSE-THROAT SPECIALIST.

WHAT IS THAT, SIR?

IT IS A HEARING AID. IT HELPS DEAF PEOPLE HEAR.

THAT EVENING—

SUPPANDI, I AM GOING TO GET MY NEPHEW FROM THE STATION. REMEMBER TO OFFER HIM SOMETHING TO DRINK WHEN WE GET BACK.

YES, SIR.

LATER—

THEY'VE HAVE COME!

SUPPANDI! WHY CAN'T YOU ASK HIM INSTEAD OF WRITING A MESSAGE?

DO YOU WANT TEA OR COFFEE?

BECAUSE HE WON'T BE ABLE TO HEAR...

...HE HAS REMOVED HIS HEARING AID.

AWK!

41

TINKLE TRICKS & TREATS ③

A

Picture (1) and picture (2) were supposed to be identical. The artist, however, has made 6 errors. Can you find them?

B Which is the odd one out?

Parasol

Hat

Sunglasses

Briefcase

C

Rahul, who is in front of Mohan, but behind John, is wearing a sweater that is similar to Qasim's, but he is not wearing a cap. Sunil is wearing a cap. Using this information, can you find out the names of each of these 5 boys?

ANSWERS ON PAGE 60

Make a paper whistle

You will need: A thin piece of paper and scissors.

1. Fold the strip of paper in half.

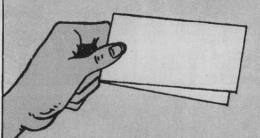

2. Cut a 'V'-shaped piece out of the folded end.

3. Hold the folded paper between the first two fingers.

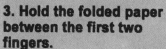

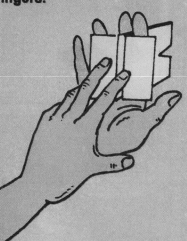

4. Fold down the two ends, press the paper to the lips and blow. You will hear a loud, shrill whistle.

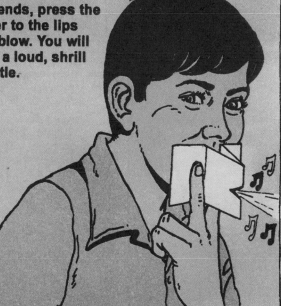

THE MAGIC HAND

SUPPANDI WAS GOING TO HIS NATIVE PLACE FOR A FEW DAYS—

HURRY, OR YOU'LL MISS YOUR TRAIN!

THERE'LL BE A BUS COMING ALONG SOON. PUT OUT YOUR HAND AND IT'LL STOP.

THAT MUST BE THE BUS!

SCREEECH

IT WORKED LIKE MAGIC! THE BUS HAS STOPPED!

HEY, YOU CAN'T BRING THAT TRUNK IN!

YOU MEAN I SHOULD LEAVE MY TRUNK HERE!

HAVE YOU NO SENSE! HOW CAN I GO TO MY NATIVE PLACE WITHOUT MY TRUNK!

LOOK, I DON'T CARE WHERE YOU'RE GOING!

GET OFF AND LET THE BUS PROCEED!

I'LL TEACH YOU A LESSON!

NOW LET'S SEE HOW THE BUS WILL MOVE WITH MY HAND OUT!

45

SLAPSTICK!

EVERYBODY THINKS I AM A FOOL. I WISH I COULD PROVE MYSELF TO BE CLEVER.

I'LL ASK THAT STRANGER IF HE CAN SHOW ME HOW.

OH, SIR...

...I WANT TO BECOME CLEVER. CAN YOU TELL ME HOW I CAN GO ABOUT IT?

SEE IF YOU CAN HIT MY HAND.

ALL RIGHT, HERE GOES...

HA! HA! SEE HOW I FOOLED YOU!

ZIP!

LATER —

THAT WAS A GOOD TRICK. I MUST TRY IT OUT ON MY BOSS.

SIR, COME. I WANT TO SHOW YOU SOMETHING REALLY CLEVER.

WHAT?

COME, EVERYBODY! WATCH THIS TRICK!

WELL?

WHAT SHALL I DO? THERE'S NO TELEPHONE POLE HERE. AH... I HAVE IT...

SEE IF YOU CAN HIT MY HAND, SIR.

ALL RIGHT.

ZZIP!

HA! HA HA HA!

WHAT A FOOL!

47

NEIGHBOUR'S FAN

SUPPANDI, THIS MONTH'S ELECTRICITY BILL IS QUITE HIGH. REMEMBER TO SWITCH OFF THE LIGHT WHEN YOU DON'T NEED IT.

OKAY, MASTER.

NEXT DAY—

WHIRRR

OH, NO!

SUPPANDI! WHY HAVE YOU LEFT THIS FAN ON? WHO WILL PAY THE BILL?

OUR NEIGHBOUR, SIR!

WHAT? BUT WHY?

IT'S HIS!

WE BORROWED IT FROM HIM REMEMBER? THEY'LL SEND THE BILL TO HIM!

YEESH!

GOOD USE

SUPPANDI'S NEW EMPLOYER WAS A TEACHER.

HAVE YOU WRITTEN THE ALPHABET, SUPPANDI?

I HAVE FINISHED WRITING ON ONE SIDE OF THE PAPER, SIR. I NEED A NEW SHEET.

YOU MUST USE BOTH SIDES OF THE PAPER, SUPPANDI. YOU CAN SAVE A SHEET THAT WAY.

YES, SIR!

LATER —

SUPPANDI! GO AND BUY ONE METRE OF CLOTH FOR YOUR SHIRT.

YES, SIR.

WHY HAVE YOU BOUGHT ONLY HALF A METRE OF CLOTH?

YOU SAID WE COULD SAVE BY USING BOTH SIDES...

...SO I THOUGHT WE COULD USE BOTH SIDES OF THIS CLOTH FOR MY SHIRT AND SAVE A METRE.

AARGH!

TINKLE TRICKS & TREATS ④

1 CAN YOU NAME THESE FRUITS?

NOW FILL THEIR NAMES IN THE RIGHT SQUARES TO COMPLETE THE FRUIT-WORD.

2 WHAT SHALL I DO? CAN YOU HELP ME REACH THE BOWL OF MILK WITHOUT GETTING MY FEET WET?

ANSWERS ON PAGE 60

3 THIS IS A LETTER A BOY WROTE TO HIS FRIEND WHO WAS ILL. HIS FRIEND FOUND IT GREAT FUN AND WANTS TO SHARE IT WITH YOU.

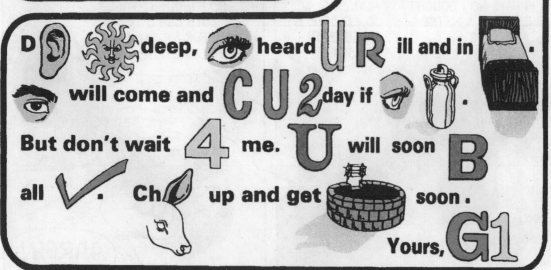

D [ear] [sun] deep, [eye] heard U R ill and in [bed].

[eye] will come and C U 2 day if [milk].

But don't wait 4 me. U will soon B

all [✓]. Ch [donkey] up and get [well] soon.

Yours, G1

4 LOOK CAREFULLY AT THIS PICTURE. HOW MANY THINGS CAN YOU FIND WHICH BEGIN WITH THE LETTER R?

5 # MAKE YOURSELF AN ACROBATIC DOLL

YOU WILL NEED: A PIECE OF CELLOPHANE PAPER 2" X 3", A PIECE OF TISSUE PAPER 2" X 3", A PAIR OF SCISSORS, A PENCIL.

A. PLACE A PIECE OF TISSUE PAPER ON THIS DOLL.

B. TRACE OUT THE OUTLINE OF THE DOLL WITH A PENCIL.

C. REMOVE THE TRACING AND PIN IT TO THE CELLOPHANE PAPER.

D. NOW CUT AWAY THE SHADED PORTION.

E. HOLD IT IN YOUR PALM AND WATCH IT FOLD UP ITS LEGS.

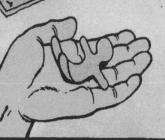

HALF A BUCKET

SUPPANDI, USE THIS NEW DETERGENT POWDER TO WASH THE CLOTHES.

BUT I DON'T KNOW HOW TO, MADAM.

JUST READ THE INSTRUCTIONS PRINTED ON THE PACKET AND FOLLOW THEM CAREFULLY.

SCRAPE SCRAPE

WHAT IS THAT STRANGE NOISE COMING FROM THE BATHROOM? LET ME GO AND SEE.

AIEE! SUPPANDI, WHAT ARE YOU DOING?

THE INSTRUCTIONS ON THE PACKET SAY THAT THE DETERGENT HAS TO BE DISSOLVED IN HALF A BUCKET OF WATER...

...SO I AM CUTTING THIS BUCKET INTO HALF.

SWOON

THE DUMBBELLS GET A FRIGHT

Script : Luis Fernandes
Illustrations : Anand Mande

IT WAS VERY KIND OF YOUR UNCLE TO INVITE US TO HIS HOUSE FOR THE WEEKEND, NATTOO.

OH, HE'S A LOVABLE OLD MAN.

HE WAS STAYING ABROAD ALL THESE YEARS. IT'S ONLY A FEW MONTHS SINCE HE RETURNED AND TOOK UP RESIDENCE IN HIS ANCESTRAL HOME.

AND WHAT A HOUSE IT IS! LIKE A PALACE! WAIT TILL YOU SEE IT.

THERE...!

I'M SEEING IT AFTER TWENTY YEARS!

KNOCK! KNOCK!

NOBODY'S HOME?

CREEEEAK

UNCLE MUST HAVE GONE OUT. COME IN, LET'S MAKE OURSELVES AT HOME.

54

HOT AND FRESH

SUPPANDI, MY BOSS WILL BE HERE ANY MINUTE. EVERYTHING WE SERVE HIM SHOULD BE FRESH AND HOT.

YOU CAN DEPEND ON ME, SIR.

SOON—

WELCOME, SIR!

PHEW! IT'S SO HOT OUTSIDE.

SUPPANDI, BRING A GLASS OF LASSI.

AND THE LASSI WAS SERVED. BUT—

YUCK!

YECOCH!

WHAT DID YOU DO TO THE LASSI?

EXACTLY WHAT YOU WANTED ME TO DO.

I HEATED IT SO IT WOULD BE FRESH AND HOT!

THE SLEEPY WATCHMAN

SUPPANDI WORKED AS A WATCHMAN FOR HIS NEW EMPLOYER.

SUPPANDI! I'VE BEEN ROBBED! DIDN'T YOU HEAR THE THIEF COME IN LAST NIGHT?

I DID, SIR!

THEN WHY DIDN'T YOU DO ANYTHING?

I DID, SIR! BUT THAT THIEF WAS A BIG LIAR.

WHAT DO YOU MEAN?

WHEN I ASKED HIM, "WHO IS THERE?"...

... HE ANSWERED, NO ONE, SIR, NO ONE!" SO I WENT BACK TO SLEEP.

YAARGH!

ANSWERS

TINKLE TRICKS & TREATS 1

A) 1. Pearl, 2. Pan, 3. Pen, 4. Pea,
5. Ear, 6. Reel, 7. Pear, 8. Oar,
9. Pole, 10. Rope.

B) 1. Japan, 2. Nepal, 3. Sri Lanka,
4. Canada, 5. Bangladesh,
6. Bhutan, 7. Pakistan.

C) A bird in hand is worth two in
the bush.

TINKLE TRICKS & TREATS 2

A) 1.   FROCK – ROCK = F
2.   BOAT – BAT = O
3.   COAT – CAT = O
4.   BEARD – BEAR = D
Answer: FOOD

B) 1. Strings 2. Tyres
3. Nest
4. Thumb 5. Boat

C) MOUSE

TINKLE TRICKS AND TREATS 3

A. 1. Flags on Tent. 2. Stripes on Tent.
3. Horse's Nostril. 4. Balloon. 5. Man's
Teeth. 6. Stripes on man's clothes

B. The briefcase is out of place. All
the other objects give protection
against the sun.

C. Qasim, Sunil,
John, Rahul,
Mohan in that
order.

TINKLE TRICKS & TREATS 4

1. Grapes, Apple, Mango, Bananas,
Pear, Plums, Orange
2. Racket, Radish, Railing, Rattle,
Ribbon, Rickshaw, Road, Rock, Roof,
Rope, Rose
3. Dear Sundeep, I heard you are ill
and in bed. I will come and see you
today if I can. But don't wait for me.
You will soon be all right. Cheer up
and get well soon.
Yours, Jeevan.

Suppandi Cleans the Fridge

GOALKEEPER

SUPPANDI WAS PLAYING FOOTBALL.

YOU BE THE GOALKEEPER, SUPPANDI.

ALL RIGHT.

GOAL!

HURRAH!

WHY DIDN'T YOU STOP THE BALL, SUPPANDI?

I FELT IT WASN'T NECESSARY!

I KNEW THE NET WOULD STOP IT!

WHAT!

62

NO ENTRY

SUPPANDI WAS OUT CYCLING WITH HIS EMPLOYER.

NO ENTRY FOR **SLOW-MOVING VEHICLES**

SUDDENLY—

HEY!

WHIZZ!!!

STOP SUPPANDI! I CAN'T KEEP UP WITH YOU.

AT LAST—

(PUFF!)...(PANT!) WHY DID YOU GO SO FAST, SUPPANDI?

BECAUSE THE ROAD SIGN SAID...

... NO ENTRY FOR SLOW-MOVING VEHICLES.

AWK!

THE DUMBBELLS

in Raising Funds!

Script: Prasad Iyer
Illustrations: Anand Mande

FOLLOWING INSTRUCTIONS

SUPPANDI, THE DOCTOR HAS PRESCRIBED THIS MEDICINE FOR MY SORE THROAT. GO AND BUY IT FROM THE CHEMIST.

YES, SIR!

THIS IS A VERY STRONG ANTIBIOTIC. IT HAS TO BE TAKEN ONLY AFTER YOU HAVE HAD A GLASS OF MILK.

OKAY.

LATER —

SUPPANDI, IT IS TIME FOR ME TO TAKE THE MEDICINE. WHERE IS IT?

IN A MINUTE, SIR!

WHAT TOOK YOU SO LONG, SUPPANDI?

I WAS FOLLOWING THE CHEMIST'S INSTRUCTIONS.

WHAT INSTRUCTIONS?

HE ASKED ME TO DRINK A GLASS OF MILK BEFORE GIVING THE MEDICINE. I WAS DOING THAT.

SUPPANDI THE SUSPICIOUS

ONE MORNING AS SUPPANDI WAS ON HIS WAY TO THE MARKET—

GIVE! GIVE TO A BLIND BEGGAR.

THAT BEGGAR IS PRETENDING TO BE BLIND. I'M SURE HE ISN'T.

HEY, YOU CHEAT, YOU ARE NOT BLIND AT ALL. YOU'RE JUST FAKING.

OF COURSE I'M BLIND.

NO, YOU'RE NOT!

YES I AM.

IF YOU CLAIM TO BE BLIND YOU WILL HAVE TO PROVE IT.

YES, I WILL!

CAN YOU SEE THAT TREE AND THE TWO BEGGARS SITTING UNDER IT?

SURE, I CAN.

WELL, I CAN'T! DOESN'T THAT PROVE I AM BLIND?

IT CERTAINLY DOES.

HERE'S A COIN FOR YOU. AND I AM SORRY FOR HAVING DOUBTED YOU.

ACHIEVING SUCCESS

ONE MORNING —

SUPPANDI! WHAT ARE YOU DOING HERE?

TRYING TO ACHIEVE SUCCESS, SIR!

BY GROVELLING ON THE GROUND? GET UP AT ONCE!

DON'T STOP ME, SIR! YESTERDAY I HEARD A WISE MAN SAY THAT YOU CAN ACHIEVE SUCCESS...

... BY FOLLOWING IN THE FOOTSTEPS OF OUR ELDERS.

HIDDEN TREASURE

HERE, SUPPANDI, I WANT YOU TO GO TO THE MARKET AND BUY SOME PROVISIONS. HERE'S FIFTY RUPEES AND TWO RUPEES FOR WAYSIDE EXPENSES.

YES, SIR.

KEEP THE FIFTY RUPEES IN YOUR CAP. BE SURE NOT TO LOSE IT.

I'LL TAKE GOOD CARE OF IT, SIR.

A LITTLE LATER —

THIS IS A LONELY ROAD. I HOPE THERE ARE NO ROBBERS AROUND.

STOP

HAND OVER ALL YOUR MONEY!

NO!

STOP! I WON'T HURT YOU. I ONLY WANT YOUR MONEY.

SO YOU THOUGHT YOU'D GET AWAY, EH? NOW HAND OVER YOUR MONEY!

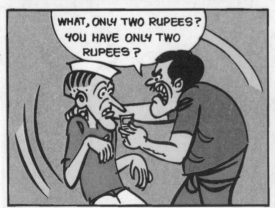

WHAT, ONLY TWO RUPEES? YOU HAVE ONLY TWO RUPEES?

ACTUALLY, I HAVE ANOTHER 50 RUPEES IN MY CAP. BUT THAT'S A SECRET!

!!

72